· *Oxford Scientific Films* ·

WILDLIFE OF
RIVERS & LAKES

Jeremy Biggs

MALLARD PRESS

MALLARD PRESS
An Imprint of BDD Promotional Book Company, Inc.,
666 Fifth Avenue, New York, NY 10103.

Mallard Press and its accompanying design and logo
are trademarks of BDD Promotional Book Company, Inc.

CLB 2336
Copyright © 1989 Colour Library Books Ltd.
© 1989 Illustrations: Oxford Scientific Films Ltd,
Long Hanborough, England.
Color separation by Hong Kong Graphic Arts Ltd, Hong Kong.
First published in the United States of America
in 1989 by The Mallard Press.
Printed and bound in Italy by Fratelli Spada, SpA.
All rights reserved.
ISBN 0 792 45027 2

Contents

This page: moose eating water plants in Yellowstone National Park.

Previous page: male fiddler crabs have one claw enlarged, which they use in territorial displays.

1
Rivers and Lakes

Water flows from the mountains to the sea over rapids and waterfalls, through tropical rain forests and rich agricultural lands. Many rivers feed lakes where the water may rest for years or, occasionally, centuries. Lakes may be the recent creations of man or natural lakes thousands of years old, created during the last glaciation. A very few of the largest lakes are millions of years old. The older the lake, the more specialized its wildlife. Lake Baikal in the USSR, which at 60 million years old is the oldest lake in the world, contains many species unique to it. Isolated from other lake plants and animals, many of the inhabitants of Baikal have been slowly changed by the environment of the lake, gradually becoming more and more suited to its special conditions. Some water enters lakes with no outlets, like the Dead Sea, where it can only escape by evaporation. As it evaporates the water leaves behind salts, which are gradually concentrated until the lake becomes saltier than the sea. In this harsh environment few species can survive, but those that do are often superabundant.

On its journey to the sea, fresh water creates habitats for many plants and animals. In the mountain lakes and rivers of the northern hemisphere sea trout and Atlantic salmon return year after year to their native *spawning* grounds. As rivers pass into the lowlands their flow slows and they begin to meander across wide flood

The spectacular Iguaçu Falls are fed by the Iguaçu River, which forms part of the border between Brazil and Argentina, in South America.

Otters inhabit lakes and rivers throughout the world.

plains. In the lowland tropics of South America the Amazon River drains water from an immense area, much of it covered by forest, providing a habitat for a huge variety of water plants and animals – including more species of fish than any other river in the world. In lowland England, tranquil rivers meander sluggishly through rich alluvial plains used for cattle grazing. Even though the land is farmed, it can still provide a habitat for wild flowers and water birds. In this man-modified, intensively farmed landscape, gravel pit lakes and reservoirs provide a refuge for wildlife. At the edge of the land, rivers and sea finally meet to create bleakly beautiful landscapes at estuaries and deltas of sand bars and great mud flats.

2
Mountain Rivers

Mountain rivers the world over have cool, clear and fast-flowing water. The rapid flow washes away most fine sediment, leaving a river bed composed mainly of pebbles, stones and boulders. The only water plants that can tolerate these conditions are mosses and liverworts, which creep over the surface of larger stones and boulders. The turbulent flow ensures that the water is always well-oxygenated; bubbles of air are constantly mixing with the water as it tumbles over rapids or waterfalls. The mosaic of stones and boulders on the river bed may appear lifeless at first, but a surprising variety of smaller invertebrate animals can be found hidden under the stones. Insects like mayflies, caddis flies and stoneflies spend their *larval* stages in water, living beneath and between the stones, emerging from the water as adults during spring and summer. Many of the species found in mountain streams are found only in water which is well-oxygenated. Turn a few stones over holding a fine-meshed pond net downstream and some of these insect larvae will be washed into the net.

Surprisingly few of these animals are exposed to the full force of the water as many shelter from the current in calm areas underneath stones

Above: the sucking loach has a mouth sucker that allows it to attach itself to rocks to resist strong currents.

Facing page: under the water, mayfly larvae graze on microscopic algae growing on the surface of stones and pebbles.

Dippers feed on invertebrate animals living on the river bottom.

or among mosses. Others seek out the thin layer of slower-flowing water, held back by friction, immediately above the surface of stones. Some mayfly larvae are especially flattened to allow them to inhabit this *boundary layer,* which is only about a sixteenth of an inch thick. They feed on microscopic *algae* growing on the surface of rocks or on particles of plant debris washed into the still areas.

The smaller animals provide food for a variety of fish and birds. Despite seeking shelter from the current, many invertebrates are washed away by the flow. In European mountain rivers they may be eaten by brown trout, which specialize in feeding on drifting invertebrates. Other fish, like minnows, feed on invertebrates on the river bed. Throughout the uplands of Europe, Asia and western North America, dippers, which look rather like large brown and white wrens, bob under the water in search of food. Dippers can walk and swim under the water, using their wings as oars and their unusually strong claws to grip stones beneath the water. They feed on the larger invertebrates, particularly caddis fly, stonefly and mayfly larvae.

3
Mountain Lakes

Mountain lakes are clear and cold, with stony margins. Many mountain lakes were created by the action of glaciers, which gouged hollows from the solid rock or enlarged river valleys and then dammed them with debris dumped as the glacier retreated. Mountain lakes are usually poor in *nutrients* because the water entering them runs off hard, *impermeable* rocks. In some lakes this water may be almost as pure as distilled water. Although often naturally acidic, many mountain lakes in Northern Europe and Canada have been made more acid by the air pollution we call "acid rain". In the clear water light penetrates as much as fifty feet beneath the surface, but on the stony bottom only hardy underwater plants can grow. The shores of mountain lakes are buffeted by wind and waves, so it is only in sheltered bays, where fine *sediments* can accumulate, that plants, like reeds, water lilies and bulrushes, can grow.

Above: microscopic algae, tiny plants no more than a 250th inch long, float freely in the open water.

Right: mountain lakes have barren, stony shores with few emergent water plants.

Arctic loons breed on remote mountain lakes throughout the northern hemisphere.

Mountain lake water appears completely clear but, if a very fine-meshed net is towed through the water, microscopic, free-floating plants and animals can be found. The plants are mostly single-celled algae, rarely more than a 250th of an inch long (many are much smaller), and can only be seen when a sample of the water is observed under a high-power microscope. In the infertile waters of mountain lakes there may be no more than 30,000 individual cells in each fluid ounce of water, compared with 30 to 60 million per fluid ounce in more fertile lowland lakes. The planktonic animals include a variety of water fleas which feed on the algae, filtering them from the water. The plankton forms the basis of the *food chain* for larger animals, particularly fish, like trout and char, and fish-eating water birds.

Remote mountain lakes throughout the northern hemisphere are breeding grounds for fish-eating birds like the common loon. Loons require the isolation of mountain lakes to give them undisturbed areas for breeding. Loons are among the most specialized of birds under water. Their powerful, webbed feet make it impossible for them to walk on land, forcing them to build their nests close to the water's edge on islands or isolated peninsulas. Diving from the surface they pursue fish through the well-illuminated, shallow water with strokes of their webbed feet.

4
Trout and Salmon

In cool, fast-flowing rivers in the northern hemisphere, trout and salmon, known collectively as salmonids, are common. In Europe there are two subspecies of "trout" (although several related species are found in North America), distinguished mainly by differences in their life cycle. The brown trout is non-migratory, living and breeding in rivers and lakes, and the sea trout is migratory, spending most of its life at sea, but returning to freshwater to breed. Atlantic salmon, which are closely related to brown and sea trout, are always migratory and also return to their native river to breed after maturing at sea. Both salmon and sea trout are believed to locate their native river by sensing the smell and taste of its water. As adults they can leap up through waterfalls, but on rivers where the flow is controlled by dams and weirs, fish ladders (a string of artificial shallow pools with a small step between each pool) must be constructed to allow migrating fish to pass. Neither salmon nor sea trout feed on their return to the river, but both take the imitation flies used by fishermen. Apparently the fish are not mistaking the fly for food, and the real reason for this behavior remains unknown.

Migrating salmon leap through waterfalls on their journey upstream to the spawning grounds.

Facing page top: salmon may spawn in very shallow water.

Above: three months after spawning, the eggs of rainbow trout begin to hatch.

Facing page bottom: brook trout are native to North America, but have been introduced to many other parts of the world.

Clean, well-oxygenated gravel is used by salmon, sea and brown trout for spawning because the eggs, once laid, need a constant supply of oxygen to hatch successfully. The eggs hatch after about three months, the young fish, known as alevins, remaining hidden in the gravel for another month. After they have emerged, the young fish, now called parr, feed on invertebrates, swimming down to the sea to mature after one to three years in the river. Sea trout and salmon return to their native rivers after one to five years at sea, some Atlantic salmon having spent this time as far afield as the coast of Greenland. Salmon can grow to a weight of 84 lb, although rod-caught specimens are usually less than this. Brown and sea trout are generally smaller and reach only 30 lb. At sea large salmon and sea trout are preyed on by seals, and perhaps also dolphins and large fish. They also face human predation, not only by river fishermen, but also from trawlers in the open ocean and netsmen working in the estuaries of rivers.

5
Lowland Rivers

A lowland river meanders through fertile agricultural land.

In the slow-flowing, warm and nutrient-rich rivers of the lowlands, plant and animal life becomes abundant and diverse. The soft, easily-weathered lowland rocks are often rich in nutrients, encouraging luxuriant growths of water plants. *Meandering* across wide flood plains, large lowland rivers develop pond-like areas of still water at their margins which, combined with areas of more rapid flow in the center of the river, provide a wide variety of habitats for plants and animals.

Marginal stands of reeds and bulrushes, water lilies and submerged pondweeds all provide habitats for invertebrate animals. In this underwater forest, water shrimps and slaters feed on decaying fragments of leaf litter, while predatory great diving beetle larvae lie camouflaged among the plants, waiting for passing prey; they feed mainly on other invertebrates, but can capture small fish. Shoals of young fish swim among the water plants, which provide them with a nursery ground and a rich supply of animal food. As they mature

they will move out into the open water of the river. The fish typical of the lowland reaches of European rivers, like roach, carp, tench, pike and perch, are all tolerant of the relatively low dissolved oxygen concentrations found in these rivers. Roach, carp and tench feed on invertebrates and plants, although their diets do change with age. The emergent bulrushes, reeds and other grasses also provide food for herbivorous water voles. In the center of the river the bottom sediment also has its characteristic inhabitants. Duck mussels live half-buried in the river bed, filtering food from the water, and mayfly larvae burrow into the softer sediments.

River cliffs, often created on river bends where meanders undercut river banks, provide areas where Eurasian kingfishers and sand martins can excavate nest tunnels. Sand martins,

relatives of swallows, feed on flying insects above the water. Many of these insects will have spent their larval life under water. Kingfishers plunge dive into the water to capture small fish (although nearly a quarter of their diet is made up of invertebrates). Invertebrate animals are also eaten by mammals. In Australian rivers, the duck-billed platypus searches under water for invertebrates with its eyes shut, relying entirely on its soft and sensitive duck-like bill to detect its food. In European rivers, water shrews also swim under water in search of invertebrates, small fish and frogs.

Left: the duck-billed platypus swims with its eyes shut, relying on its sensitive bill to detect food.

Below: European kingfishers nest in burrows excavated in river banks. Each chick needs about fifteen fish every day.

6

Lowland Lakes

Lowland lakes are warm, *turbid* and have silty or sandy margins. Water plants, including microscopic algae, grow rapidly and in large quantities in these fertile waters, providing habitats for many animals. Fish and invertebrates use plants as spawning sites; dragonflies and water boatmen, for example, often insert their eggs into the stems and leaves of water plants. The surfaces of water plants are colonized by microscopic forests of algae, like lichens growing on trees in a forest. The algae are grazed by snails, mayfly larvae and caddis fly larvae. Water plants also shelter slow-moving predatory water stick insects and water scorpions.

Invertebrate animals and fish are abundant in lowland lakes which are, as a consequence, excellent feeding and breeding grounds for water birds. In the shallowest water, dense stands of reeds, rushes and sedges grow and on some lakes may cover huge areas. Sixty square miles of Austria's shallow Lake Neusiedlersee, almost half its total area, is covered in reed beds which provide a habitat for rare birds like bearded tits, marsh harriers and bitterns. In deeper water, beyond the fringing reed-swamp, floating-leaved plants grow. On tropical and sub-tropical lakes lily trotters and purple gallinules can be seen stepping delicately from lily pad to lily pad. Most kingfishers (there are over eighty species around the world) hunt from perches, but around African lowland lakes pied kingfishers hover and dive for fish. This allows them to feed much further from the shore than kingfishers dependent on perches from which to dive.

On lowland lakes in northern Europe diving ducks, like pochard and tufted ducks, feed on plants and animals under the water, while mallard and shoveler dabble at the water surface, sifting seeds and small animals from the water. The swamp and fen at the edge of shallow water provides abundant nest sites for ducks and wading birds. Loch Leven, a fertile lowland lake in Scotland, has the largest concentration of breeding ducks in Britain. In Europe the fish fauna of lowland lakes is like that of lowland rivers, including members of the carp family, pike, perch and, occasionally, wels catfish, which can grow to over twelve feet in length and weigh up to 660 lb.

Above: reed warblers suspend their nests from the stems of common reeds.

Facing page top left: the marsh hawk preys on small mammals and birds like this mallard.

Facing page top right: the long toes of the purple gallinule allow it to spread its weight as it walks over water lilies.

Facing page bottom: pike are predators that feed almost exclusively on other fish.

7
Plants in the Water

Water plants grow in distinctive zones in and around rivers and lakes. At the water's edge tall, emergent reeds, rushes and sedges grow rooted in the shallow water. Around mountain lakes, with their predominantly rocky or sandy shores, this *community* is restricted to sheltered areas where there is less exposure to waves. With an inexhaustible supply of water, and fully exposed to the light, reed swamp grows rapidly in lowland lakes and is one of the most *productive* plant communities in the world. Beyond this marginal

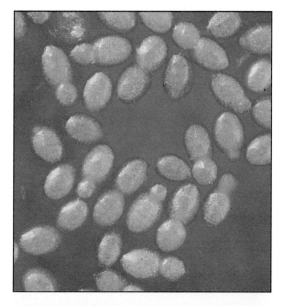

Right: the world's smallest flowering plant is the rootless duckweed.

Below: giant Victoria lilies, found in South America, have leaves which may be up to six feet in diameter.

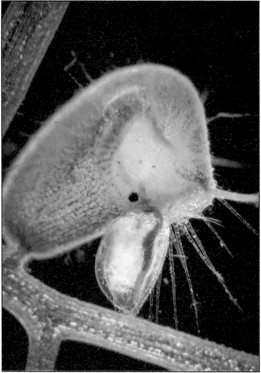

zone of *emergent plants*, in slightly deeper water, floating-leaved plants like water lilies and duckweeds grow if conditions are sufficiently sheltered. In the deeper water, plants with leaves completely submerged, like Canadian pondweed and water milfoil, may be found. Plants growing beneath the water in rivers, like the white-flowered water crowfoot – members of the buttercup family – have streamlined, flexible and finely-divided leaves which offer little resistance to the flow of water.

Although water plants are never short of water, they may be short of light. Light falling on the surface of a river or lake is very quickly absorbed as it passes through the water. Even in the clearest lakes light does not penetrate more than thirty to forty-five feet and in rivers it is often much less. Submerged plants rarely grow more than fifteen feet below the water surface because so little light penetrates beyond that depth. In some lakes and ponds, particularly those polluted by fertilizers washed out of the soil on farmland, microscopic planktonic algae compete with submerged water plants for light. In these conditions planktonic algae can be sufficiently abundant for these microscopic plants to color the water green and, collectively, shade out all the large submerged water plants. Water plants growing in upland lakes can be short of nutrients so some, like bladderworts, supplement their nutrient supply by feeding on animals, trapping and digesting water fleas in tiny bladders attached to their stems.

Floating-leaved plants have abundant supplies of light and moisture but can only grow in calm water. They range in size from the rootless duckweed, which has fronds just a twentieth of an inch across and is one of the smallest flowering plants in the world, to the gigantic Victoria lilies of South America, the leaves of which are three to six feet wide.

Left and top left: bladderwort is a carnivorous plant that captures water fleas and other small animals in tiny bladders that grow among its leaves.

8
The River Flood Plain

Water is always present in the main channel of a river, but only spills onto the flood plain when the river is in spate. In Europe flood plains, which often have rich, *alluvial* soils laid down by centuries of flooding, have mostly been converted to agricultural grasslands, often used for grazing cattle. Where agriculture is non-intensive and farmers have not treated pastures with fertilizers and pesticides, these grasslands are still rich in wildlife. Wading birds, like snipe and redshank, breed on the riverside pastures, while meadows cut for hay blaze with wild flowers in the spring and summer. Male snipe have spectacular territorial display flights, using their tail feathers to make a bleating sound called "drumming", which they use instead of song. In some river valleys winter flooding is controlled and the flood water used to fertilize the pastures, which are known as water meadows.

Flood plains may have oxbow lakes, remnants of old river meanders cut off from the river when the meanders changed position on the flood plain. These lakes may be nurseries for young fish (the fish get into the lakes when flood water spills onto the flood plain) and breeding grounds for amphibians as well as water plants and animals unable to survive in moving water. Britain has only six species of native frogs, toads and newts but all, except the natterjack toad, may be found in these oxbow lakes. If fish are abundant, common toads may become the dominant members of the amphibian fauna. Toad tadpoles are unpalatable to fish and are able to survive, and may become extremely abundant, whereas frog tadpoles and the larvae of the three species of newts are eaten by fish. Like all ponds and lakes, oxbow lakes eventually fill with silt from river flood water and decaying leaf litter.

Several tropical and subtropical rivers have vast flood plains over which water spreads in the rainy season. The Sudd Swamps on the Nile in southern Sudan consist of 4,000 square miles of seasonally-flooded wetland. The swamps support an enormous variety of large mammals,

Above: hippos spend most of their time resting in or near to water. They feed on dry land for just five or six hours during the night.

Above right: common frogs spawn in the early spring in western Europe, each female laying about 2,000 eggs.

Facing page: Brazil's Pantanal floodplain in full flood.

including elephants, buffalo, reedbuck, waterbuck and about half a million tiang antelope, making this one of the biggest populations of large mammals in the world. Alongside many African rivers the flood plain grasslands are also used by the hippopotamus for night-time grazing. During the day, hippos need to return to the water as their thin skin rapidly loses moisture in dry air.

9
Great Lakes

The world's largest lakes have many special features associated with their great size and age. Standing on their shores it is easy to feel that one is standing on the sea shore. Large waves break onto their beaches and the far shores are beyond the horizon. Lake Baikal in the USSR, which is over 5,200 feet deep at its deepest point and between sixty and sixty-five million years old, is the deepest lake on earth. It holds about one fifth of the world's fresh water and houses many species of plants and animals found nowhere else in the world (*endemics*). These include the freshwater Baikal seal (most seals live in the oceans) and a freshwater shrimp the size of a crayfish. Most of the endemic species are associated with the open water or the depths of the lake, while around the lake shore plants and animals found throughout Europe and Asia are common.

Lake Tanganyika, in the African Rift Valley, which is 420 miles long and up to 4,700 feet deep, has endemic species of water snails, caddis flies, snakes and fish. Many of the endemic species of snails, which have thickened and heavily ornamented shells, more closely resemble marine mollusks than typical freshwater species. This probably reflects the fact that the shores of large lakes rather resemble the wave-washed rocky shores of the sea, where strong shells are an important adaptation. Lake Malawi, also in the African Rift Valley, has 245 species of fish – more than any other lake – many of which are endemic. The majority of the endemic species are cichlids and display a remarkable variety of feeding habits, including eating the scales and nibbling the fins of other species.

Top: a very wide variety of species of cichlid fish can be found in Lake Malawi.

Facing page: Lake Baikal is home to species of animals and plants found nowhere else .

Above: waves break on the shore of Lake Superior.

In contrast to the ancient great lakes, the North American Great Lakes are quite young, having been formed during the last glacial period, 10,000 to 15,000 years ago. They have a combined area equal to the British Isles but, because of their immaturity, have no endemic species. However, over a hundred species of fish occur naturally in the Great Lakes and support a successful commercial fishery, which centers around members of the salmon and trout family (salmonids). Despite their size, several of the North American Great Lakes, especially Lake Erie – which has a human population of twelve million in its catchment – have been polluted by the huge quantities of urban and industrial waste discharged into them from the cities on their shores.

10

The Amazon

The Amazon River in South America has the biggest catchment in the world, collecting water from about 2,700,000 square miles. Tropical rain-forest covers approximately two-thirds of this catchment, although the proportion is constantly shrinking as land is cleared for agriculture. The tributaries of the Amazon rise in the Andes and flow across the width of the continent, eventually discharging 190,000 tons of water into the sea every second.

The Amazon supports more species of fish than any other river in the world. Many of these depend as much on the forest as on the river. About 19,000 square miles of the forest is flooded in the rainy season and fish swim through the shallow flood water to feed on fruits, seeds and flowers that have fallen into the water. Some fish are even responsible for the dispersal of the seeds of plants, taking on a role more commonly associated with birds, bats and insects.

Where forest gives way to grasslands, capybaras, the world's largest rodents, may be found, closely cropping the riverside grasses. Capybaras, although relatives of guinea pigs, stand eighteen inches high at the shoulder and have brown, bristly hairs. Like hippos, their eyes, ears and nose are placed on the top of their heads, allowing them to rest in the water almost

The Amazon River drains an area thirty times the size of Britain.

Capybaras, the worlds largest rodents, are good swimmers, and are able to stay under water for up to five minutes.

completely submerged. In the water, manatees, slow-moving seal-like animals which are most closely related to elephants, graze on water plants. They are seven to nine feet long and weigh up to half a ton but, despite their bulk, they are placid, slow-moving animals. Manatees, known locally as "fish-cows", are the only herbivorous mammals that live exclusively in the water. They are long-lived (some live more

than thirty years in captivity) and give birth only once every two years. Due to their slow rate of reproduction they are vulnerable to hunting, which can rapidly reduce their numbers.

Giant otters, about five feet long long when fully grown, hunt slow-moving fish through shallow creeks. They also move into the flooded forest during the wet season in search of fish to feed on. Their numbers, although not exactly known, are thought to have been greatly reduced by hunting for their valuable waterproof pelt.

11
Where River and Ocean Meet

At the edge of the land, rivers may form open estuaries or, if laden with large quantities of sediment, build deltas like those of the Nile or the Mississippi. Estuaries are influenced both by salt and freshwater and provide a harsh environment for invertebrates and fish: too salty for those from freshwater and not salty enough for those from the sea. In the mud, silt and sand of estuaries relatively few species of invertebrates are present – mostly worms, snails and small crustaceans – but they are often extremely abundant and provide a rich source of food for water birds, especially waders. The many different species of waders which overwinter or stop over on migration on mud flats feed on different foods, so reducing competition between species. Waders with short bills, like ringed plovers, feed mainly on surface-dwelling crustaceans, while those with longer bills, like curlews and godwits, feed on deeper-burrowing shellfish and marine worms.

River estuaries include some of the most spectacular wildlife habitats in the world, although many are threatened by drainage – especially for agriculture. In Europe, major wetlands have developed at the mouth of the River Danube in Rumania, covering nearly one-and-a-quarter million acres. Immense floating stands of reeds and bulrushes occupy much of

Above: anhingas are one of the few water birds that do not have waterproof feathers. After swimming under water they dry and reposition their feathers by spreading their wings.
Facing page: manatees browse on freshwater plants and sea grasses in large rivers and shallow coastal waters in the tropics.

this area. At the mouth of the River Rhone, on the Mediterranean coast of France, the Camargue covers 345,000 acres and supports the most northerly population of flamingos in the world. The River Guadalavir, the largest river in Spain, supplies water to the marshlands of the Coto Donana. Covering 600,000 acres, this area of seasonally flooded marshes and dunes provides feeding and breeding grounds for terns, waders, ducks and many other water birds. It is a major wintering ground for graylag geese, which breed in the Arctic, and provides food for some 60,000 of these birds in winter. Like many coastal wetlands it is threatened by human activities, including drainage for agriculture, pollution of its water supply by farm pesticides, and building developments.

In many parts of the tropics, river estuaries are fringed by mangrove forests. Mangroves tolerate high concentrations of salts and bind sediments with their networks of air-breathing roots, so protecting coastlines from erosion and flooding. Over 2,000 species of fish, invertebrates and epiphytic plants depend on mangroves.

Mangroves obtain oxygen through aerial roots, which allows them to inhabit mud that lacks oxygen.

12
Soda Lakes

Most rivers flow to the sea but some, like the River Jordan, which flows into the Dead Sea in the Middle East, flow into inland lakes with no outflow. Water can escape from these lakes only by evaporation, concentrating salt in the lake. Dead Sea water, for example, is ten times saltier than sea water. Surprisingly, saline lakes are quite common and there is almost as much saline lake water in the world as all the freshwater in lakes and rivers. Soda lakes can be found on all continents and are as much a feature of cold climates as of hot climates. Perhaps the most famous saline lake is Lake Nakuru in Kenya, which supports huge numbers of lesser flamingos. Saline water is a harsh environment for freshwater plants and animals, favoring the development of enormous populations of the small number of species adapted to these conditions. These include a limited variety of microscopic blue-green algae, water fleas, brine shrimps and flamingos. Brine shrimps are graceful invertebrate animals, about half an inch long, which swim on their backs and use their many limbs to filter algae from the water. Brine shrimps are very vulnerable to predators and survive only in very salty water or temporary pools, where there are few other animals, particularly fish, to prey on them.

Flamingos are almost always found on saline lakes because of their highly-specialized method of feeding. As their individual food items are so small they must be present in huge quantities for the birds to be able to gather enough food. Such quantities of these microscopic organisms are found regularly only in saline lakes. Flamingos feed with their heads upside down, straining the superabundance of planktonic algae or water fleas from the water. Their bills

Lesser flamingos, with their heads and bills upside-down, filter algae from the water.

have rows of fringed plates inside them which form fine filters and, using their tongues as pistons, flamingos pump up to eight gallons of water through these filters every minute, extracting their microscopic food from the water. Different species have different-sized filters and feed on different sized particles. The lesser flamingo of the African Rift Valley lakes feeds mainly on algae, whereas the greater flamingo feeds on larger food items, such as brine shrimps. Flamingos are not restricted to hot climates and, in mountain regions in South America, Chilean flamingos are found on high altitude saline lakes.

Facing page top: up to two million lesser flamingos may gather around Lake Nakuru in Kenya.
Facing page bottom: streams in the Namib Desert terminate in salt pans before being able to reach the sea.

13

Man-Made Lakes

In lowland Britain, and throughout much of northwest Europe, almost all larger lakes are man-made; man-made lakes include gravel pit lakes, reservoirs and ornamental lakes. Even some apparently natural lakes are man-made; the Norfolk Broads in East Anglia in England, for example, were created by medieval peat digging and are now one of the most important wetland areas in the country. In intensively managed landscapes even the more recently created lakes are vital refuges for wetland wildlife, especially water birds. Within thirty years of construction or excavation a diverse wetland ecosystem can develop and, as these waters increase in age, they become gradually more valuable for wildlife.

In Britain, reservoirs created in the last thirty years, like Abberton in Essex and Rutland Water in the East Midlands, have become refuges of international importance for overwintering ducks like mallard, shoveler, widgeon and teal. Many of these birds migrate to Britain from continental Europe to escape harsh winter conditions and to find relatively warm open water throughout the winter. These newly created lakes also support abundant populations of fish, which provide food for birds like great crested grebes, herons and goosanders. The great crested grebe, rare in Britain at the beginning of the 20th century because of the demand for its head plumes in the millinery trade, has become a particularly

Below left: common terns breed around inland gravel pit lakes in southern Britain.

Below: man-made reservoirs are often important winter refuges for wildfowl.

Canada geese, found throughout North America, have been introduced to Britain, where they are now a common sight on man-made lakes.

characteristic sight at reservoirs and gravel pit lakes. A ban on the trade in its head plumes at the beginning of the century was important in allowing a recovery in the population of grebes, while the subsequent creation of many new lakes has allowed the population to reach its greatest size this century.

Shingle islands in gravel pit lakes provide nesting sites for common terns and little ringed plovers. The creation of gravel pit lakes has allowed terns, which normally breed near to the sea, to colonize inland areas, and has allowed little ringed plovers to colonize Britain for the first time. In continental Europe this species breeds on river shingle, a rare habitat in lowland Britain, and until the widespread excavation of gravel pits, little ringed plovers did not breed in Britain. However, bare sand and gravel is a transitory habitat and, unless specially maintained, is quickly colonized by plants and animals.

Glossary

ALGAE Simple plants, many of which are single-celled and microscopic, which do not have distinct roots, stems or leaves.

ALLUVIAL Composed of fine sediments which settle out from river flood water (usually refers to river flood plains).

BOUNDARY LAYER A thin layer, no more than a sixteenth of an inch thick, of slow-moving water held back by friction around stones in fast-flowing rivers.

COMMUNITY Plants and animals living close together which require similar environmental conditions to survive.

EMERGENT PLANTS Plants that usually grow with their roots in shallow water and their leaves emerging into the air.

ENDEMIC Plants and animals found only in small areas of the world (especially islands).

FOOD CHAIN The capture of the energy of the sun by plants and its transfer by feeding through grazing animals to predatory animals.

IMPERMEABLE Of a rock, like granite, which water does not penetrate.

LARVA The pre-adult stage of animals like insects, fish and amphibians which hatch from eggs.

MEANDERS Naturally formed loops and bends in rivers.

NUTRIENTS Chemicals dissolved in the water which, although present only in minute quantities, are essential for the growth of plants and animals.

PRODUCTIVE Of an ecosystem, usually warm, moist and rich in nutrients, where plants grow rapidly.

SEDIMENTS Silt, sand, pebbles and decaying plant and animal remains which are deposited in rivers and lakes.

SPAWNING Egg-laying, usually under water, by fish and amphibians.

TURBID Of water clouded by large quantities of suspended sediment or microscopic algae.